Printed and Published in Great Britain by D.C. THOMSON & CO., LTD.,
185 Fleet Street, London EC4A 2HS. © D. C. THOMSON & CO. LTD. 1977.

95p

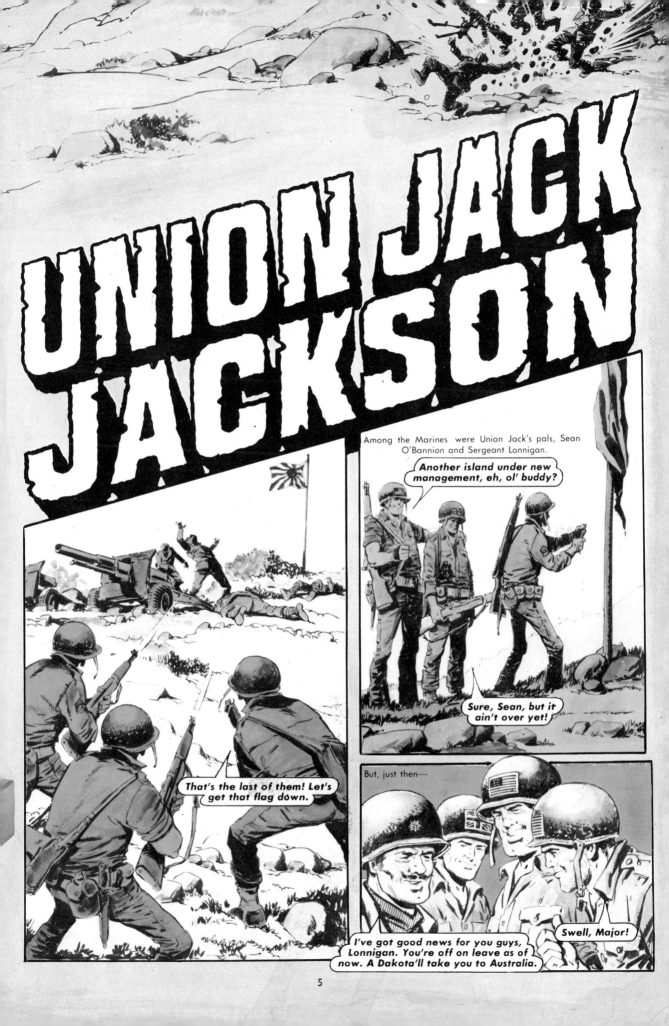

UNION JACK JACKSON

That's the last of them! Let's get that flag down.

Among the Marines were Union Jack's pals, Sean O'Bannion and Sergeant Lonnigan.

Another island under new management, eh, ol' buddy?

Sure, Sean, but it ain't over yet!

But, just then—

I've got good news for you guys, Lonnigan. You're off on leave as of now. A Dakota'll take you to Australia.

Swell, Major!

That afternoon, as the three Marines made their way to the plane—

Make way there!

Captain Hartz! You'd think he'd been where it all happens, instead of sitting in an office!

The Dakota was soon airborne, but as it approached New Guinea—

I'm really gonna enjoy myself, Sarge. They say them Aussies give us servicemen a real good welcome.

We gotta get there first! Fighters coming in!

Jap Zeros! We haven't got a chance!

We're hit!

Aussie Wildcats! The Zero's are runnin' for it!

Too late, though—we've had it! I'll have to crashland in the jungle!

The Japs an' the Aussies are slugging it out down there—and we're coming down on the wrong side of the line!

6

This is the only clearing for miles. Hope I can stop her in time!

AARGH!

Morgan's arm's broken.

And the pilot's unconscious. We've got to get him clear—the plane could blow any second!

Jackson! Come back here, yah stupid Limey!

We can't survive in the jungle without our packs, Sean!

She's burning, buddy! Hurry it up!

I ain't exactly hangin' about, mate!

The Japs'll be along any time, Sarge. I don't think we should wait for 'em. We'll rig a stretcher to —

Just a minute, soldier. I'm the only officer here so I'm in charge!

Yes, sir, of course. We've got to reach the Aussies and the Japs are in the way. Which way do you suggest we go?

We're not going anywhere! We're going to surrender!

Marines never surrender, Captain Hartz! You stay if you like—we'll take our chances in the jungle! Move out, you guys!

8

There was another shock in store for Tim when he landed back at base—

You fool, Jones! That wasn't a German plane you shot down. It was a Beaufighter! We found the wreckage where you said you saw the Junkers crash.

That's impossible! I know they look alike, but I'm sure I attacked a Junkers!

Tim was charged and court-martialled—

One of our Beaufighters disappeared in the area where you claimed to have shot down a Junkers. You made a terrible mistake, therefore you are suspended from flying duties.

But had Tim made a mistake? The true story of what happened wasn't revealed until after the war when the Allies discovered . . .

Hitler's Secret Files

MISSION No 48682!

It all began in April, 1945, when top German pilot Hans Schuler was called to a meeting with Hitler in Berlin.

This is a mission of the utmost importance. You must not fail, Schuler.

You can depend on me, mein Fuhrer.

Schuler flew out to an airstrip at a secret research centre near Magdeburg.

Welcome to Group Nibelung, Major Schuler. I take it you have been fully briefed?

Ja. I know that the fate of Germany hinges on my success.

Schuler's aircraft was a specially-converted Junkers Ju 88.

This bomber is heavily laden. I might not get it off the ground.

I made it! Heil Hitler!

But as Schuler flew on, Tim Jones' Typhoon came into view—

Himmel! A British plane!

AAARGH! I'm hit!

A few hours later—

Wait! That steeple! I almost crashed into it that night. The wreck must be near here.

Right. We'll stop and make enquiries.

This old fisherman says he knows where there's a wrecked plane. He'll take us there in his boat.

Later—

Look over there—in the reeds! It's the tail of a Jerry plane!

So it WAS a Ju 88 I shot down! Phew! Look at the size of that bomb!

I shall make an inspection. You others will stay here.

The bomb is safe. The impact did not disengage the release toggles, thereby activating the timer. If it had, this area would have become a wilderness.

What's he talking about, Group Captain?

Isn't it obvious, Jones? That is an atomic bomb!

An atomic bomb? Good grief! But where was it going to be dropped?

The bomb was Hitler's last chance of saving the war, Jones. He intended to wipe out London! I'll see that your name is cleared. You deserve it!

THE END.

16

As Lord Peter Flint, Britain's top wartime secret agent, code-named Warlord, reports to his boss one day—

Hmm! Useful looking torch— just the job for the blackout!

Kingpin—don't switch it on, old chap!

Ye gods—a snake! Keep clear, Flint!

It's just a toy— present for my nephew. But his mother wouldn't let me give it to him.

I'm not surprised—gave me a nasty turn. Now, down to business. Little mission for you.

This is Professor Descard, one of France's top atomic scientists. He went into hiding when France was occupied but the Nazis are on to him now.

And now he wants out?

Yes! He contacted the local resistance and asked for help in escaping. We need him as badly as the Germans. Get him out, Flint, fast!

18

That night, Flint was landed at a rendezvous in France—

Be back here same time tomorrow night. If I'm not around, don't wait. It'll mean something has gone wrong.

Now, where's my resistance contact—great Scot, where did you spring from?

I am your contact. Armand's the name. Come, I have a lorry waiting over here.

Are we likely to be stopped by patrols? What about the curfew?

There has been no trouble for months so security is slack. The Boche prefer to stay by their guardroom fires!

You had strict orders not to do anything which might jeopardise my mission. There'll be Germans all over the place now. Get off the streets, fast!

Don't worry—we are nearly at my home!

An explosion! What the devil's going on?

Ah, well, our group has just blown up part of the barracks. A chance offered itself—it was too good to miss.

Sacre bleu! Road blocks out already. I have ammunition hidden among the potatoes. I will have to crash through!

No, do that and they will be after us. Pull up—I'll try to bluff them.

19

While one German began to search the lorry, another searched Flint—

Ah, ha! What is this in your pocket?

Nothing, sir, nothing!

You call this nothing!

It is only a torch—please don't switch it on.

The other German, curious, came down from the lorry—

Aaargh! Himmel! A snake!

Teufel!

I asked you not to—it is only a toy. A present for a small boy. Now you have broken it.

Don't be insolent! Get out of my sight before I arrest you both!

Five minutes later, they were in Armand's house—

Your stupid sabotage at the barracks has added to my difficulties. Jerry will be all over the streets. I just hope they haven't found Professor Descard yet.

Armand! In the morning I want a cart, long ladders, a bucket of water and some rags. I'm going to become a window cleaner.

If you say so, m'sieur!

Next morning—

There is the house where the professor lodges.

I don't like the look of those two Germans on the corner. They could be watching the place.

Madame, please fetch your lodger. I must speak with him on a matter of life or death.

He is not here. He is at the market!

Descard is at the market. We'll go there now. Oh, oh, trouble—looks like the Jerries are closing in.

Schnell! Open the door!

That settles it! We must intercept the professor. The Gestapo have traced him.

Flint and Armand dumped the barrow and—

We're in luck—got him right away. Over there at that vegetable stall.

But even as Flint moved towards the professor—

More trouble, Armand. Three truckloads of German troops have just rushed into the square!

Into the trucks! Move! Schnell!

Jerry seems to be rounding up hostages, so it's not the professor they're after yet.

But they've got him just the same!

Why are you doing this? We have done nothing?

You are being punished for last night's outrage at the barracks. An example is being made of you.

Come back—we cannot help the professor now. We will be arrested!

Precisely—that way I'll stay close to the professor.

Stop! Release those people! You have no right!

We've every right—and you can join your friends if you're that fond of them!

What a situation! The Gestapo is searching the town for Descard and he's been picked up without them knowing it.

Flint made himself known to the professor—

For the time being you are as safe here as anywhere. I'll look for an opportunity for our escape later.

The prisoners were driven to a railway siding—

You are being sent to a labour camp. If there is any more sabotage in this town, others will suffer your fate.

Once aboard the train, it's next stop Germany, Warlord. If we're to escape it must be now.

No, Armand. The line passes the spot where we were to be picked up and the German guards' carriage is at the end of the train. A bad mistake!

It is not far now. At the top of this gradient we are only five miles from your rendezvous—and we are still locked in here!

Not for long! Voila—one saw blade!

Soon have this bar sawn through.

Good luck, m'sieur. Our captors are in for a surprise, no?

Provided I don't fall off, yes!

Flint made his way along the roofs to the end of the train—

Buttons are a useful way of disguising plastic explosive—and I've got detonators in my shoes. Now if I blow the coupling before we reach the top of the slope, the carriage with all the Germans in it will run back down the hill.

Next moment—

Our carriage has broken loose. We are running backwards. Put on the brakes.

There are no brakes!

That shovel will come in handy.

Now for the driver and his pal.

Mon dieu! A madman!

AAARGH!

No—but I'll get pretty mad if you don't stop the train.

Everyone out! Hurry! Get home before the Jerries get you.

Armand, make them all scatter and and head for home. Professor, you come with me. We'll hide out until our plane comes. It'll be dark soon.

Flint ran back to the engine and started the train moving back the way it had come—

THE END

25

CALLING WARLORD AGENTS

HELLO AGAIN, CHAPS. PHEW, AM I GLAD TO BE HOME! I'VE JUST FINISHED A GRUELLING ADVANCED KARATE COURSE IN TOKIO AND BOY IT WAS HARD! I WAS MATCHED AGAINST THREE JAPANESE CHAMPIONS AND DID THEY KNOW THEIR STUFF! LUCKILY, THOUGH, I WAS AT PEAK FITNESS FOR THE TRIP AND MANAGED TO GIVE A GOOD ACCOUNT OF MYSELF.

WHILE ON THE SUBJECT OF FITNESS, HOW ARE THE EXERCISES GOING? YOU SHOULD BE VERY GOOD AT THEM BY NOW, SO HERE ARE A FEW MORE DIFFICULT ONES TO ADD TO YOUR TRAINING SCHEDULE. THEY ARE SOME OF THE EXERCISES I DO TO KEEP ME FIGHTING FIT FOR KARATE.

IMPORTANT
YOU MUST BE PROPERLY WARMED UP BEFORE ATTEMPTING THESE EXERCISES! DO YOUR OTHER EXERCISES FIRST

1—Sit on the floor and spread your legs wide. Take a firm hold of the left ankle, with BOTH hands and pull your head to your knee. Repeat ten times, then do the same on the right.

2—With your legs spread wide, put both hands on the floor, between the feet. Keeping your knees locked back, bounce your forehead off your hands ten times. N.B. If you can't reach your hands, do NOT force things! It takes practice.

3—Standing with your legs shoulder width apart, bend backwards as far as you can, pushing the hips forward with your hands. Hold the position for a few seconds, then bring the body forward and put the palms of your hands on the floor. Repeat five times.

4—Spread the feet about twice shoulder width. Drop the hips and bounce, pressing hips down with hands.

5—From previous position, turn the left foot and straighten the leg, dropping the hips farther. Bounce gently, trying to get left calf to the floor. Repeat on right side, changing every five bounces.

6—Lie flat on your back, with hands stretched away behind your head. Tensing the stomach muscles, lift the feet six inches in the air. Open and close ten times then rest. Repeat once.

I hate to see people left out so here's an easy code for non-agents to try. It's a simple code where A=Q, B=R and so on. Try to decode the following message. As an example, I've done the first word for you.

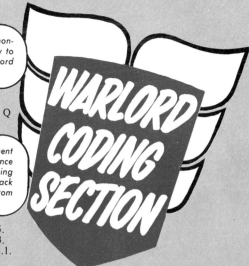

WARLORD CODING SECTION

OPERATION

Flint's message reads: EFUHQJYED WHKRUH Q SECFBUJU IKSSUII. HUJKHDYDW JE RQIU.

Manage, chaps? Simple really, isn't it? There's a Secret Agent feature, including coded messages in 'Warlord' every week. Once you're really good at codes, you will be able to attempt the following message. This is a harder one for experienced 'Warlord' agents. Crack this one—IF YOU CAN! The solution to both codes are at the bottom of the page.

6.16.19.18.21.21.5.'6.   18.   5.2.1.   22.3.22.4.14.   18.20.22.3.5.
17.12.5.   23.18.16.24.6.   5.19.22.   24.26.23.23.22.7.   26.3.
6.5.26.3.16.5..   18.   6.22.11.22.7.22.   19.18.3.15.26.16.18.1.
26.3.   '2.12.7.   23.26.3.22.   2.21.   10.2.7.24..

MAP AND COMPASS

Long winter nights can be an absolute bore so here's how you can use your spare time to good advantage. Secret agents must be able to find their way across all types of terrain, so here are a few basic hints on finding your way—with or without map and compass!

MAP-READING

First of all, always take note of the scale of your map—e.g. one inch to one mile, one inch to four miles or the new metric ones. Also check the list of symbols on your map. Practise with an Ordnance Survey map of your own area.

Always study your route thoroughly before setting out. Make sure that if you have a river to cross, there is a bridge. Obvious, you may think, but an easy thing to overlook! Also, check hills for steepness and height. This is easily done. If the contour lines are very close together then the incline is very steep. On the other hand, if they are spread out, then the gradient is slight. Heights can be ascertained by counting the contour lines. They are at intervals of fifty feet on one-inch maps.

WITH COMPASS.

The first thing to remember when using a compass is that the needle points to MAGNETIC NORTH. Ordnance Survey maps are based on TRUE north. However, each map shows the number of degrees variation from magnetic north for that part of the country. This is called the magnetic variation. For instance, if the variation is 8 degrees west, then you add 8 degrees to your course. i.e. if your map bearing is 90 degrees then your actual course will be 98 degrees.

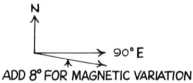

ADD 8° FOR MAGNETIC VARIATION

TO FIND YOUR DIRECTION OF TRAVEL

Imagine you are on top of hill (A) in the sketch, and you want to get to church (B). Stand facing the church and when your compass settles at north, read the number of degrees indicating the direction of travel to the church. This is your compass bearing. Simply walk this course checking your bearing every time you meet an obstacle.

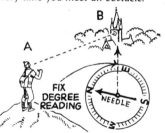

FIX DEGREE READING

NEEDLE

WITHOUT A COMPASS
By The Sun: (Northern Hemisphere)

The sun rises in the east and sets in the west, moving about fifteen degrees every hour. At 6 a.m. G.M.T. (Add one hour to all times for British Summer Time) the sun is in the east. At noon it is due south and at 6 p.m. in the west. Intermediate directions can be calculated using these times. e.g. at 9 a.m. the sun will be half way between east and south, i.e. south-east!

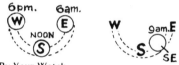

By Your Watch:

A greater degree of accuracy is possible with your watch. Simply lay your watch flat with the hour hand pointing to the sun. South will be half way between the hour hand and twelve o'clock. (Remember to adjust for accuracy by putting your watch back an hour in summer time).

WARNING

Do NOT venture into wild hill country on your own in winter. Wait until spring before trying out your new skills. And always go in a party, preferably with an adult. You should also be suitably clothed—warm jersey, water and windproof jacket, balaclava, gloves and leather boots. Toodle-pip!

CODING SECTION SOLUTIONS

Work 'em out correctly? Well done!

A	B	C	D	E	F	G	H	I	J	K	L	M	N	O	P	Q	R	S	T	U	V	W	X	Y	Z
18	17	16	15	22	21	20	19	26	25	24	23	4	3	2	1	8	7	6	5	12	11	10	9	14	13

Schafft's a top enemy agent but lacks the killer instinct. A severe handicap in our line of work.

QRSTUVWXYZABCDEFGHIJKLMNOP
ABCDEFGHIJKLMNOPQRSTUVWXYZ

Operation Gruber a complete success. Returning to base.

THE TORNADO

THE MAKING OF A FIGHTER

It costs half a million pounds to train a pilot to fly a plane like the R.A.F.'s latest multi role combat aircraft, the Tornado (above), so only the best are chosen. This is the story of how the R.A.F. turns a raw recruit into a highly-trained fighter pilot.

The famous Royal Air Force College at Cranwell in Lincolnshire.

A recruit's first act on joining the R.A.F. is to swear an oath of allegiance to the Queen.

otos—M.O.D..Command Public
elations H.Q. R.A.F. Germany..B.A.C.

PILOT

Before taking to the air, the trainee pilot has to "go to school." Here, an instructor explains an aircraft's control system.

This is a Phantom Simulator terrain contoured map. Using this, a trainee pilot can practise low-level flying without leaving the ground!

Before taking to the air, every possible safety check is made. Here, a pilot tests his flight harness.

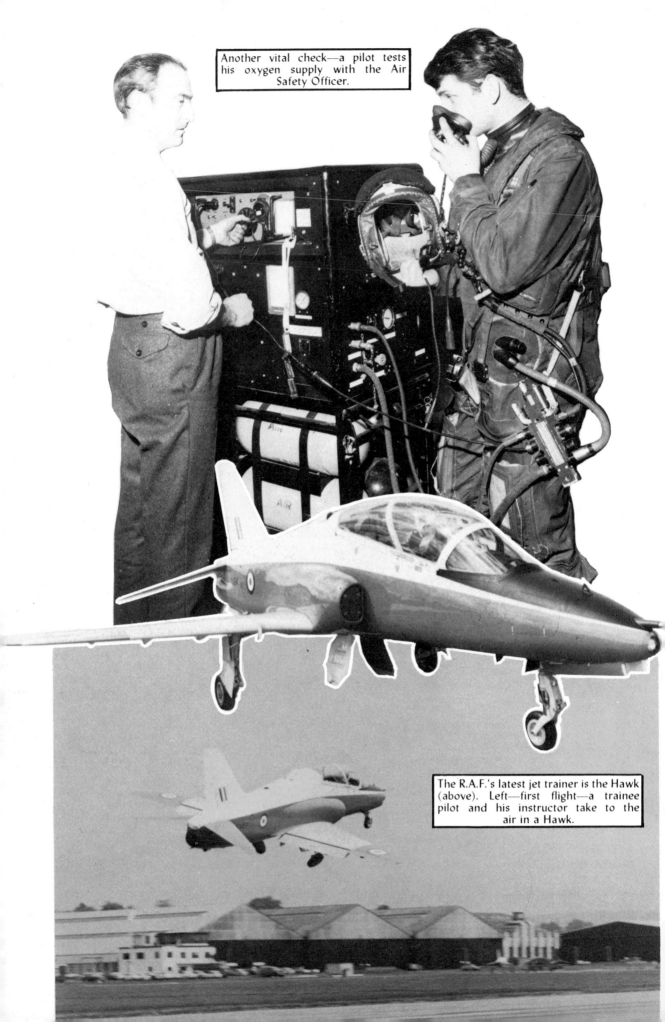

Another vital check—a pilot tests his oxygen supply with the Air Safety Officer.

The R.A.F.'s latest jet trainer is the Hawk (above). Left—first flight—a trainee pilot and his instructor take to the air in a Hawk.

The moment of truth! A young pilot makes a last-minute check with his instructor before taking off on his first solo flight.

An important part in the making of a fighter pilot is weapons training. This is done on a Hawk like the one shown here, armed with four Matra rocket pods.

The final stage in a fighter pilot's training is reached when he is posted to an operational conversion unit to specialise in a particular type of aircraft. Here a young pilot climbs into a Harrier.

THE JAGUAR

THE PHANTOM

At last the fully-fledged fighter pilot is posted to an operational squadron to fly "fast jets" such as the Jaguar (top) and the Phantom (below).

The aircrew of a Phantom—tough, resourceful and highly-trained.

But the training of a fighter pilot never really stops. The aircrews of the R.A.F. practise constantly to keep in peak condition. This superb action shot shows a Harrier firing its rockets during exercises.

Cold and calculating, Squadron-Leader "Killer" Kane, the R.A.F.'s most ruthless pilot, screams into the attack as a German raiding force crosses the English Channel—

Remember, chaps, go for the pilots! Planes can be replaced —men can't!

KILLER KANE

That'll do for them! They won't get far with that lot in their belly!

The dogfight was watched by Luftwaffe Chief, Reichmarschall Goering—

Himmel! It cannot be true! Nine fighters and a bomber force routed by three measly Spitfires!

The raid had been laid on specially for Goering's benefit. He was furious when the planes returned—

Dummkopf! Blockhead! What happened?

It must have been one of their ace squadrons, sir. Their leader shot four of our planes down before we knew where we were!

It must've been this man, Killer Kane. HE MUST BE DESTROYED!

Meanwhile, Kane was testing his reflexes with a spot of clay-pigeon shooting—

The C.O.'s a terrific shot. He hasn't missed once yet.

Suddenly—

Look out, sir!

Blimey! A Focke-Wulf fighter!

He's dropped something! I bet it's propaganda leaflets.

Next day, Kane led his Squadron on an attack on Wolff's base—

But—

What's all the to-do, Kane? Some sort of message from the jolly old Hun, eh?

SQUADRON LEADER KANE, I CHALLENGE YOU TO A DUEL AT 1400 HOURS ON JUNE 10TH 1941 OVER OSTEND. MY AIRCRAFT HAS A WOLF'S HEAD ON THE FUSELAGE *Erich Wolff* (MAJOR)

Wolff's one of Goering's blue-eyed boys—a top ace! You must accept!

Not a chance, Haversham-Phipps. My job's to fight the Luftwaffe, not indulge in personal battles!

I've no intention of accepting Wolff's challenge but there's no harm in acknowledging his message!

So the coward refuses to fight! Well, we'll see about that!

Later, in the Officers' Mess at Kane's station—

The officers are steering clear of me. They think I've let the Squadron down by refusing Wolff's challenge!

Next day, Kane went into a nearby village—

It's Wolff! He's shooting up that school bus!

UURGH!

That swine dropped a message! Says he'll shoot up the village again unless somebody called Kane meets him in single combat!

So, that night—

My plan has worked! Kane has accepted at last!

Next day, as Kane headed for the rendezvous—

Hello, Ground Control—let me know if any more planes come skulking around.

Just then, a captured British merchantman was steaming through the rendezvous area—

Kane's in for a surprise! By being catapulted from the ship I won't be picked up by the British radar till it's too late!

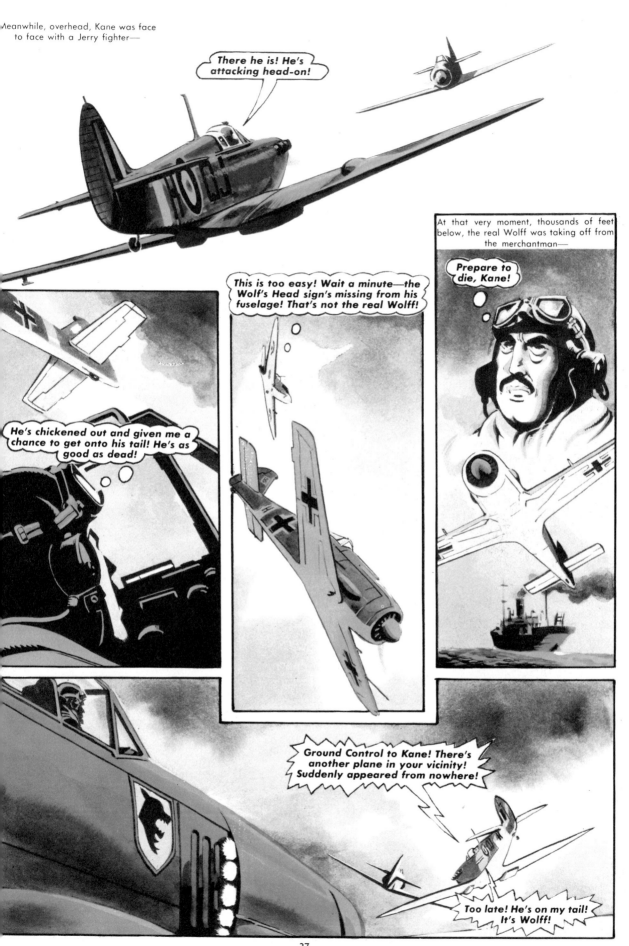

Meanwhile, overhead, Kane was face to face with a Jerry fighter—

There he is! He's attacking head-on!

At that very moment, thousands of feet below, the real Wolff was taking off from the merchantman—

Prepare to die, Kane!

This is too easy! Wait a minute—the Wolf's Head sign's missing from his fuselage! That's not the real Wolff!

He's chickened out and given me a chance to get onto his tail! He's as good as dead!

Ground Control to Kane! There's another plane in your vicinity! Suddenly appeared from nowhere!

Too late! He's on my tail! It's Wolff!

THE END

COMBAT

Photographs from Our Intrepid Front-line Cameramen

MULE TRAIN. Units of the British First Army push on into Tunisia while Churchill tanks undergo repairs in the background.

Lt.-General Montgomery, Commander of the British Eighth Army, inspects the sea defence guns at Benghazi.

CAMERA
THE DESERT

BOGGED DOWN! Using portable sand
tracks to get a heavily laden truck
over an area of soft sand.

Armoured cars taking up positions on
the perimeter just before Rommel's
siege of Tobruk in 1941!

British units advance into Sidi Barrani passing the monument commemorating the capture of the town by the Italians only months before.

A signaller radios back to his base as his forward observation post comes under artillery attack by the Afrika Korps.

A sad end for this fighting machine. Knocked out, this Italian tank was covered with boulders and used as a road-block.

Two weeks later, at their base in Malta, Drake's M.T.B. was ready for action again—almost!

Two weeks I've been kicking my heels, Harris. Now we're ready to go and I'm waiting for two new sailors.

Yes, sir. But they're only one minute late. In fact, I think I see them coming now.

Thanks for the lift, mate!

Never mind the niceties. Get aboard, quickly!

Sorry, sir! Seamen gunners Elliott and Graham reporting for duty!

Lieutenant Harris, the Number One. Don't worry about the skipper. Do your job well and you'll be okay. Foul up and he'll have your guts for garters.

The M.T.B. put to sea immediately.

Tell you something, Jock. I've heard tales about this Drake bloke. Bit of a madcap, I believe!

Stark raving bonkers I heard. He'll fight anything that's got a swastika on it!

Stark raving bonkers, am I? Right, Elliott and Graham. I hope you can shoot that Oerlikon as well as you can shoot your mouths. I'll be watching you!

Aye, aye, sir!

45

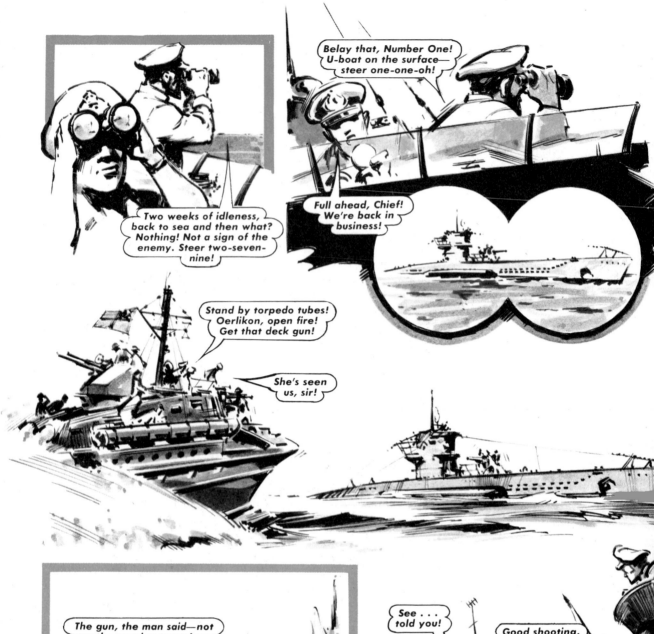

THE END

FAMOUS FIGHTING MEN AND THEIR WEAPONS

U.S. MARINE RAIDER

Operating solely in the Pacific during World War Two, the Raiders were volunteers from existing Marine Corps units and were trained to fight and survive in the most hazardous conditions. Their main tasks were to spearhead amphibious landings and to raid enemy-held islands. This they did with notable success until they were disbanded in 1944.

M I carbine. ·30 calibre. Accurate range—300 yds.

Garand semi-automatic rifle. ·30 calibre. Maximum range—1,200 yds.

M 3 submachine-gun. ·45 calibre. Range—100 yds.

Smith and Wesson M1917 revolver. 6 shot. ·45 calibre.

Colt M1911A automatic pistol. 8 shot. ·45 calibre.

Browning automatic rifle. ·30 calibre. Accurate range—800 yds.

ENEMY TERRITORY ON BOARD THE EXPRESS

Meanwhile, at a prisoner-of-war camp in Masteune, in enemy-occupied France—

Keep your hands on your heads and move along quickly, Britisher schweinhunds! Schnell!

Among the prisoners were three Commandos, Sergeant Don Brett, Lofty Carver and Chunk Martin—

I reckon once this train gets to Kenegsberg, we get dead, Lofty.

There's only one thing for it, lads. As soon as we get a chance, we make a break for it!

Blimey, Sarge, you're a real barrel of fun! Just what's needed to lift a bloke's morale — I don't think!

Aye—IF we get a chance!

Let me do the talking—my German's pretty good. Any of you lot know how to drive a train?

I can, Sarge. I worked on the railways before the war.

But as Don and his men made for the train—

Halt—er, sir. That train is being held for General Meyer.

Ja, ja. It is all right. I have been ordered to move it to a safe position.

A few minutes later—

So far, so good.

What a bit of luck! There's a railway map here. We're on our way back to France!

Some time later—

There's a bloomin' train followin' us! Get the sarge on the intercom!

Jerry troop-train coming up fast!

Well, you've got a gun—use it!

But—

Missed! Load her up fast!

Wowee! What a smash-up! They won't bother us now!

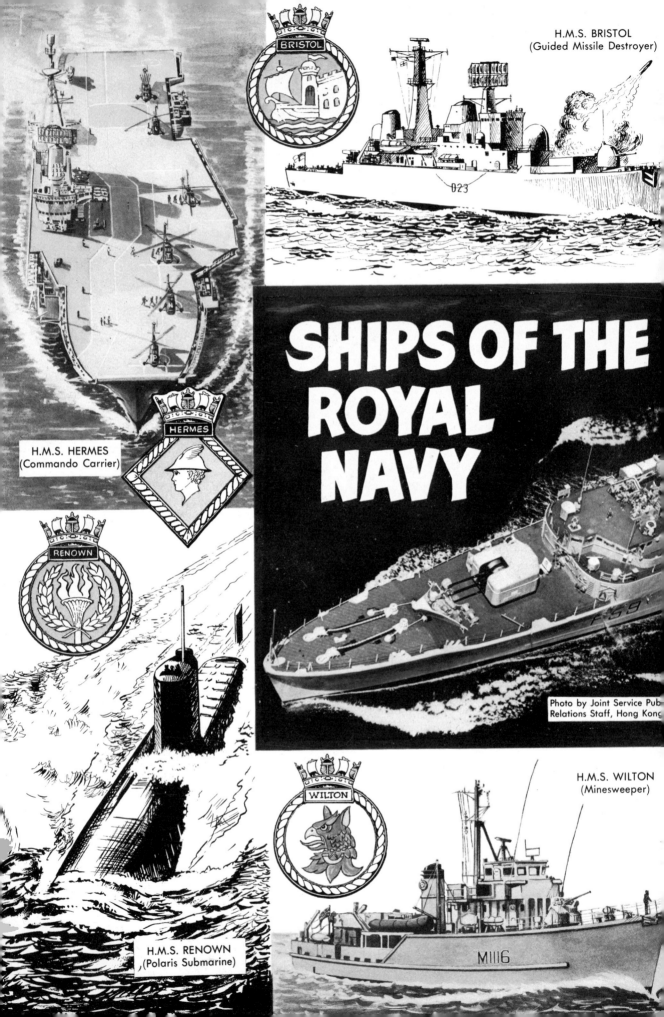

H.M.S. BRISTOL
(Guided Missile Destroyer)

BRISTOL

SHIPS OF THE ROYAL NAVY

HERMES

H.M.S. HERMES
(Commando Carrier)

RENOWN

Photo by Joint Service Pub
Relations Staff, Hong Kong

WILTON

H.M.S. WILTON
(Minesweeper)

H.M.S. RENOWN
(Polaris Submarine)

H.M.S. ANTELOPE
(Frigate)

H.M.S. SHEFFIELD
(Destroyer)

H.M.S. FEARLESS
(Assault Ship)

H.M.S. CHICHESTER
(Frigate)

H.M.S. DIDO
(Frigate)

KILLER

THE STORY OF A WEAPON IN ACTION

December, 1941. Heavy underwater explosions rock the British battle-ships, Queen Elizabeth and Valiant, at anchor in Alexandria harbour. They are victims of a weapon new to naval warfare—the two-man guided torpedoes of the Italian Navy.

PIGS

TWO-MAN TORPEDOES

Known as 'Pigs' by their crews, the torpedoes had a range of only 20 miles and were normally carried by a parent ship and released near their target. An electric motor gave them a speed of over 3 knots. A 700 lb. charge was carried in the detachable nose section and was clamped to the keel of the enemy vessel.

Two years later two young Italian officers, veteran Pig-jockeys found themselves in an awkward position.

Since your government has chosen to change sides and become enemies of the Reich, you two are confined to the base until further notice.

We are now German prisoners, Pico—just like those English down there.

I've been wondering why they've been so busy loading that old liner, Cesare! How about finding out?

And so—

Psst! Englishman— over here!

I haven't a clue what's going on, mates. All I know is we've loaded a few hundred tons of blooming cement aboard that tub.

Cement! That tells us enough, my friend. Thank you.

A block-ship, eh, Pico! Before pulling out, the Germans obviously intend sinking the old Esterella where she will block the channel and prevent this port being used by the Allies.

Those Nazis have no respect for Italian property. My friend, I have an idea—let us find Vasari!

Petty Officer Vasari was the team's electrician and mechanic.

Yes, sir, the equipment is in order. The Germans allow me in daily for maintenance, but with a guard to keep an eye on me.

Thank you, Chief—er, there is no need to mention this conversation to anybody.

That night, there was stealthy movement about the naval officers' quarters—

Quickly and quietly does it! There's no-one about!

This is where our equipment is stored. We'll enter by the side-door once that sentry has passed.

We have no key so we will have to unscrew the lock.

Suddenly—

Do not move or I fire.

Blast! The sentry!

60

Phew! Lucky this marker buoy was close. Now I have to get Cesare ashore.

He's started breathing again. He should come round soon.

A burly figure loomed as they reached the quay.

Just as well I decided to stick around.

Good man, Vasari! Help me with Lieutenant Cesare. He's a bit groggy.

We'll be safe in the hills, gentlemen. I know ways out of this base the Germans have never dreamed of!

You rascal, Vasari. I always suspected you were the brains behind the local black market.

Done it! They'll never be able to block the channel now before the Allies arrive. Our last little pig certainly delivered the bacon.

THE END

A RACE AGAINST TIME AND THE JAPS FOR THE MEN OF....

FORCE VIPER!

DUEL TO THE DEATH! Over the jungles of Burma in 1942 a Spitfire and a Jap Zero are locked together in a grim struggle for life . . .

64

..., six men of Force Viper, ...arty of river borne ...es, watched as the Zero ...ed earthwards. They ...led by Sergeant Bill Hammond.

Good shooting! He's got the Zero!

But—

The Spitfire's in trouble too! He's losing height!

He's coming down! Come on, we may be able to rescue the pilot.

Suddenly—

YAARGH!

Japs on the bank—and they've caught us out in the open!

...e men of Force Viper were ...ardened veterans and their ...ly fire took toll of the Japs.

AAARGH!

YUUNNGH!

One of 'em's getting away, Sarge.

Yeah, but he'll be back—with the rest of his slimy yellow mates!

The cheeky blighters have busted our engine. It's paddle power from here on, lads.

Looks like some native villagers have beaten us to it. They've rescued the pilot.

Message from H.Q., sir. That Spit that came down was on special proving trials. It was packed with secret equipment. We're to try to destroy the aircraft to ensure it doesn't fall into enemy hands.

The plane isn't badly damaged. It'd be a shame to destroy it.

Then we won't destroy it. We'll take it back with us!

What? But how? It won't fly and we can't carry it!

With the villagers helping, Hammond organised the building of a raft.

That's the way, lads. Another four logs should do the trick!

When the raft was completed—

Okay, easy now. Let's get the Spit onto the trestles.

Later—

Sarge! Japs! Dozens of 'em! Coming downriver in boats!

Everybody into the trees—quickly! We can ambush the Japs!

But—

It's no use, Sarge. We haven't got the firepower.

I'll cover you!

Okay! Everybody back to the raft!

COMBAT

Photographs from Our Intrepid Front-line Cameramen

SNIPER! American troops use the old hat-trick to flush out a German marksman.

AL VESUVIO

Advancing British units ride in victory through an Italian town in 1943.

CAMERA

WESTERN EUROPE

VICTORY! The Nazi Swastika is lowered for the last time in the town of Kleve as the Allies push on towards the Rhine.

American and British mortar teams raining shells down upon enemy positions.

British paratroops take cover in a shell-hole in the hopeless battle for Arnhem.

CHARGE! American soldiers race across a field strewn with German dead.

The long trek through the Apennines for British troops as they strive to push the Germans out of Italy.

Mopping-up operations in a French town after D-Day—a far cry from the retreat from Dunkirk in 1940. (See picture on left.)

73

A FEW MONTHS AFT[ER]
THE END OF THE WA[R]
MICHAEL CATER STE[PPED]
FORWARD TO RECEI[VE]
THE GEORGE CROSS [ON]
BEHALF OF HIS DEA[D]
SON. HALL CATER [WAS]
A HERO NOW...BU[T]
ONCE HE'D BEEN
BRANDED —

TRAI[TOR]

secret files

WHEN GERMANY WAS DEFEATED IN 1945, A BATCH OF TOP SECRET FILES WAS FOUND BY THE VICTORIOUS ALLIES IN HITLER'S RUINED BUNKER IN BERLIN...AND SOME BAFFLING MYSTERIES OF THE WAR WERE SOLVED. ONE SUCH STORY FOLLOWS....

TOR!

Keil was a British agent . . .

I've picked up some important details on that pilotless flying bomb being designed by the Luftwaffe.

That should interest London. I'll take my transmitter out into the countryside this afternoon.

London keep asking the identity of the contact who supplies me with such top-grade information.

Decline to answer. I joined the Nazis to help destroy them and I've no wish to be blown by a leak in London.

But Buchner of the Gestapo had never trusted Cater.

That's the fourth time in a month that Cater has visited the dentist. He either has very bad teeth or my suspicions about him have been right all along.

Two nights later, the air-raid sirens wailed over Berlin.

The bombers will be here soon, Hall. We are evacuating to the shelter.

I'll join you as soon as I've finished this report.

Everyone's gone to the shelter. Now I can take a look round.

This is where top secret Luftwaffe information is kept.

Interesting. The FZG-76 is to go into mass production—12,000 to be stockpiled for an attack on Britain commencing on June 12th.

Later, in a nearby air-raid shelter—

I must order you to come with me, Herr Keil.

Oh—er, certainly.

Ach so! Cater sees his dentist in the middle of an air raid. It must be very important.

AUSGANG

Sorry about the rush, but London must have my news without delay if a defence is to be set up against the flying bombs.

Transmitting from my cellar should be safe during a raid, Hall. Detector vans are not likely to be roving.

But, ten minutes later—

Now we pay Herr Keil a little visit.

Just as Keil finished transmitting—

OPEN UP! STATE POLICE!

Burn your papers, Keil, I'll try to hold 'em off.

AAAARGH!

They've burned everything! We'll never know what information they stole.

Herr Buchner! The Englishman is still alive.

Buchner reported to Adolf Hitler—

We have interrogated Cater, but he refuses to talk. I suggest we execute the swine.

Very well. But if the true story gets out the world will know he made fools of us. Instead say that he died fighting for Germany on the Russian front. Then he will always be known as a traitor.

Furthermore, the Fuhrer has declared that you shall be recorded officially as heroically slain in action.

I suppose he'd look rather foolish otherwise. Well, do get on with it, old fellow.

FIRE!

And so, thanks to Hitler's secret files, Michael Cater leaves Buckingham Palace, knowing that his son will never again be called a traitor.

THE END

FAMOUS FIGHTING MEN AND THEIR WEAPONS

GURKHA

These sturdy warriors from the mountains of Nepal have served in the British Army for more than a hundred years. With their deadly kukri knives they are masters of close-quarter fighting, as Britain's enemies have found to their cost. During the Second World War, Gurkhas fought in North Africa, Italy and the Far East. The Gurkha charging into action is also armed with a Lee Enfield Rifle No. 4 Mk. I .303 calibre.

3 inch mortar.
Weight of projectile—10 lbs.
Rate of fire—5 r.p.m.
Range—1,600 yds.

Government issue fighting kukri with wooden handle and leather covered scabbard.

Decorative kukri with horn handle and silver mounted scabbard bearing the badge of the Gurkha Rifles.

A giant ceremonial kukri with inlaid brass decoration on the blade.

Half an hour later—

It was a good move taking this route, Sarge! The road back there's even more jammed!

And there's the road we're heading for, but look—somebody's beaten us to it!

Jerries! We're cut off from the battery!

Worse than that. They're going to hit the new position from behind. We've got to stop them!

Crash action! I'll act as gun-layer—you get the ammo ready.

Load! High explosive—charge three!

Shaw's first shot was a near miss.

An ambush!

Load again. Quickly, before he sees us!

But his second was spot on!

AAGH!

We're being fired on from up on the hill. Spread out—schnell!

The second tank's getting a bit close, Sarge!

I'm on to him! He won't get much closer!

YEEAAH!

Got him!

Suddenly—

Jacko's been hit!

UGH!

Get down! The infantry have out-flanked us!

84

And so—

Two hours later—

THE END

At that moment—

Englanders! We can ambush them. Stay behind cover and put one man to guard the prisoners.

Jawohl, Herr Leutnant!

Tommy went into action!

I've got to warn our boys or they won't stand a chance!

OOF!

IT'S A JERRY AMBUSH! TAKE COVER!

Tommy's warning came just in time—

Get down! We're under fire!

If you keep 'em busy, I'll try to outflank 'em.

Good thinking, Lofty. Off you go.

But now Tommy was in big trouble!

Tommy! The guard is recovering! He's going for his gun! Stop him!

Too late, Englander! I have the gun!

And now you die!

But, at that moment—

Tommy! Get out of the way!

LOFTY!

BOMB

LONDON BURNS
AS NAZI BOMBERS
COME OVER NIGHT AFTER NIGHT
TO DROP THEIR DEADLY LOADS OF HIGH
EXPLOSIVE ON THE BATTERED CITY...

SEARCHLIGHTS PROBE THE BLACKNESS AND ANTI-AIRCRAFT GUNS KEEP UP A CONSTANT BARRAGE.... BUT STILL THE BOMBERS GET THROUGH....

SQUAD

.....AND ON THIS NIGHT, THE ENEMY DROPS A DEADLY NEW WEAPON .....THE PARACHUTE MINE!

One of these mines scraped down the side of a large office block in the City . . . and stuck there, suspended by its parachute!

That's when the call went out for the Bomb Squad'—No 6 Bomb Disposal Section led by Sergeant Bob Barton.

This one's nasty, Sergeant.

They're all nasty—every blooming one of them!

German naval mine with instant detonation fuses. When it strikes, it blows!

We'll need a long fire escape ladder. It's your turn, Tubby. Take Ringer with you.

Don't forget, Tubby—treat it gently.

It's all right for you! You're down there, we're up here!

Barton hurried up to the roof—

It's still holding. Gotta pray it'll hold long enough or we'll all be blown to kingdom come!

THE END

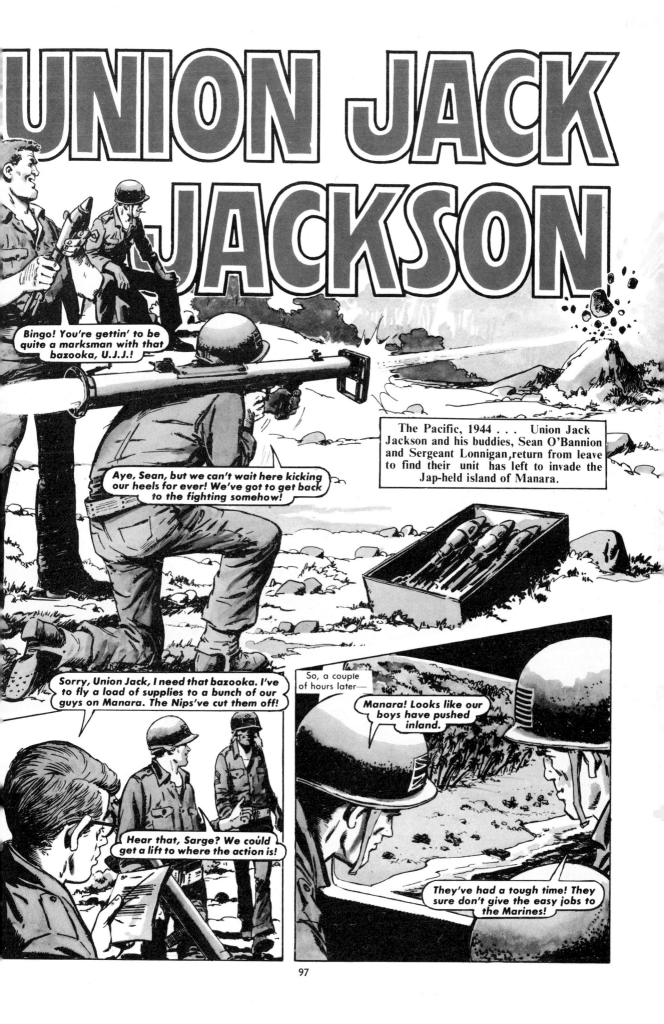

UNION JACK JACKSON

Bingo! You're gettin' to be quite a marksman with that bazooka, U.J.J.!

The Pacific, 1944 . . . Union Jack Jackson and his buddies, Sean O'Bannion and Sergeant Lonnigan, return from leave to find their unit has left to invade the Jap-held island of Manara.

Aye, Sean, but we can't wait here kicking our heels for ever! We've got to get back to the fighting somehow!

Sorry, Union Jack, I need that bazooka. I've to fly a load of supplies to a bunch of our guys on Manara. The Nips've cut them off!

Hear that, Sarge? We could get a lift to where the action is!

So, a couple of hours later—

Manara! Looks like our boys have pushed inland.

They've had a tough time! They sure don't give the easy jobs to the Marines!

You've started a rock-slide! That's fixed 'em!

One of them's gettin' away!

We've got to stop him! He'll bring more of them down on us!

A truck! Well, he ain't goin' anywhere!

Got 'im! He won't live through that lot!

Wrecked! A pity—we could've used a good set of wheels.

Maybe we still can, Sarge. We could make ourselves a handcart!

Using tools from the supplies, the three Marines soon fashioned themselves a small wagon—

Nice work, U.J.J.! We sure couldn't have humped all these crates on our backs!

FAMOUS FIGHTING MEN AND THEIR WEAPONS

JAPANESE INFANTRYMAN

Men like this, fearless in action and expert in jungle warfare, were responsible for Japan's amazing successes in the Far East in the early years of World War Two. A tough and ruthless enemy, the Japanese soldier would usually fight to the death rather than surrender.

Type 14 automatic pistol. 8 shot. 8 mm. calibre.

Type 94 automatic pistol. 6 shot. 8 mm. calibre.

Type 38 Arisaka rifle. 6·5 mm. calibre. Accurate range—500 yds.

Type 100 submachine-gun. 8 mm. calibre. Range—about 100 yds.

Type 97 81 mm. mortar. Weight of projectile—6·9 lbs. Range—over 1,500 yds.

Type 92 heavy machine-gun. 7·7 mm. calibre. Range—over 1,500 yds. Rate of fire—450 r.p.m.

Type 11 Nambu light machine-gun. 6·5 mm. calibre. Range—1500 metres. Rate of fire—500 r.p.m.

Standard hand grenade.

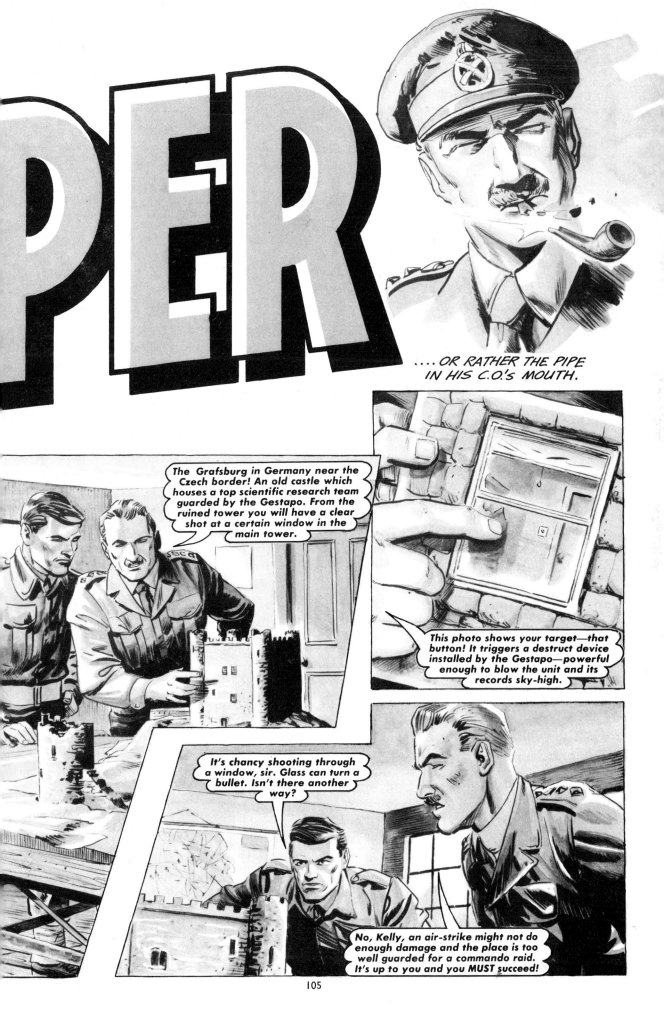

PER

.... OR RATHER THE PIPE IN HIS C.O.'s MOUTH.

The Grafsburg in Germany near the Czech border! An old castle which houses a top scientific research team guarded by the Gestapo. From the ruined tower you will have a clear shot at a certain window in the main tower.

This photo shows your target—that button! It triggers a destruct device installed by the Gestapo—powerful enough to blow the unit and its records sky-high.

It's chancy shooting through a window, sir. Glass can turn a bullet. Isn't there another way?

No, Kelly, an air-strike might not do enough damage and the place is too well guarded for a commando raid. It's up to you and you MUST succeed!

And so the next night—

There's the signal! Glad to see these Czech partisans are on the ball.

I am Hacha, your guide. We shall use what is left of the night to start for the Grafsburg. Keep an eye out for Germans.

Kelly and his guide moved stealthily through the night.

Two hours later—

There is the Grafsburg. Now we wait for . . .

Hold it! Someone is coming. Back into the bushes.

A flipping dog!

Wait. He is with our man.

It is a regular patrol. They will not find us. We move on when they are past.

Doktor Muller. I am here with the man of whom we spoke.

A little reminder, Herr Doktor. This is a British hand grenade. Any sign of treachery and I shall stuff it down your throat!

Ach—so. You know the way. I shall make contact with you at dawn when you are in position.

Your suspicion is natural, but totally unfounded, I can assure you. Now I must return or the guardroom will wonder why I am taking so long to walk my dog.

Englishman, I do not know what to make of that little Hun. He is one of the scientists at Grafsburg. He told us all we know of the place. I do not trust him but it was decided his information was worth gambling two lives—yours and mine.

Entering through an old grating, they made their way along an ancient drain.

Those steps take us up into the ruined tower.

There—the Grafsburg. Stay low, Englishman. A Battalion of Waffen SS guard it and they have sharp eyes!

Came the dawn—

Now do you see, Englishman? A minefield, barbed wire, weapon bunkers—the castle is a steel nut which only an armoured division could crack.

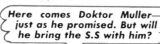

Here comes Doktor Muller—just as he promised. But will he bring the S.S with him?

I appreciate your help, Doctor, but why are you, a German, helping us to destroy your countrymen?

The research undertaken here has found the means of producing an explosive force from the atom. I regard myself as a good German in helping to keep such tremendous power from the Nazis.

There is the window!

I see it—but there's a big problem—

The blind's down. I can't see the target!

107

THE END

COMBAT

Devastation in the heart of London after a heavy German bombing raid.

Despite the bombing, London buses carried on as usual—sometimes!

SCRAMBLE! SCRAMBLE! British pilots race for their planes as another enemy raid begins.

CAMERA

THE HOME FRONT

Londoners somehow managed to retain their sense of humour.

½ COUPON

WHEN WE WERE YOUNG AND IN OUR PRIME WE WOULD BUY 3 SUITS AT A TIME

BUT NOW WE HAVE GOT HITLER TO BEAT WE MAKE ONE SUIT LAST 52 WEEKS

Even the blitz couldn't stop football matches being played! Here, workmen clear Millwall's pitch after a bomb had hit the terracing.

TAKING COVER! When the bombs came, Londoners had to seek refuge in air-raid shelters, cellars and underground stations.

The heroes of the blitz. Firemen risked their lives daily to save homes, property and lives.

SHOT DOWN! A Heinkel He III, a victim of Britain's air defences.

Rescue workers bring a victim out of the debris that was once a home.

St. Paul's Cathedral . . . amazingly unscathed amid the bomb-shattered City of London.

SEPECAT **JAGUAR** SINGLE-SEAT TACTICAL STRIKE FIGHTER OF 54 SQUADRON.

PLANES

AND THEIR

HAWKER SIDDELEY **ANDOVER** Mk 1 SHORT-RANGE TACTICAL TRANSPORT OF 32 SQUADRON.

HAWKER SIDDELE **NIMROD** Mk LONG-RANGE MARIT PATROL AIRCRAF OF 203 SQUADR

HAWKER SIDDELEY **HARRIER** GR. Mk 3 SINGLE-SEAT V/STOL STRIKE AND RECONNAISSANCE AIRCRAFT OF 4 SQUADRON.

HANDLEY PAGE **VICTOR** K. Mk 1A FLIGHT REFUELLING TANKER OF 57 SQUADRON.

114

OF THE R.A.F. BADGES

McDONNELL DOUGLAS **PHANTOM** F G R. Mk 2
TWO-SEATER ALL-WEATHER MULTI-PURPOSE
FIGHTER OF 43 SQUADRON.

HAWKER SIDDELEY **HAWK**
TWO-SEAT ALL-WEATHER MULTI-
PURPOSE TRAINER OF THE ROYAL
AIR FORCE COLLEGE.

HAWKER SIDDELEY
BUCCANEER
S.Mk 2B TWO-SEAT STRIKE
AND RECONNAISSANCE
AIRCRAFT OF 12
SQUADRON.

LOCKHEED **HERCULES** C. Mk 1
MEDIUM-TO LONG-RANGE TACTICAL
TRANSPORT OF 47 SQUADRON.

(M.O.D. PHOTO)

...APRIL, 1943...GERMAN U-BOAT 379 IS ATTACKED BY A WELLINGTON BOMBER...

...U-379 CRASH-DIVES STRAIGHT INTO A SANDBANK... AND STIC THERE, UNABLE TO MO

THAT'S HOW A GERMAN U-BOAT FELL INTACT INTO BRITISH HANDS....AND SIGNALLED THE START OF ANOTHER DANGEROUS MISSION FOR LORD PETER FLINT, BRITAIN'S TOP WARTIME SECRET AGENT.....

Code-name

A week after the capture, Flint met his boss, the mysterious Kingpin, at the dockyard where the U-boat was being repaired—

You'll use the U-boat to penetrate the impregnable submarine pens at Hangerstrom Fiord in Norway, Flint. That's where Jerry is converting his subs to take a new glider bomb.

I take it you want me to destroy the whole shooting match, Kingpin old bean?

...THE CREW SURRENDERS UNDER THE GUNS OF THE WELLINGTON AND A ROYAL NAVY SHIP STEAMS TO THE SCENE...

WARLORD

Naturally! The U-boat will be packed with explosives—a floating bomb. You'll have a skeleton crew, all volunteers.

This is a tough one, all right. Getting out will be the problem, but I'm sure I'll think of something.

Next night, the sub moved off—

Do you think they'll succeed in getting in, sir?

Yes! The Germans don't know we have U 379 and we captured all her code-books and so on intact. The Royal Navy has been warned not to attack her. Flint will do it if anyone can!

Stop engines! Set the fuses on the explosives and then all hands on deck.

Their second task was to secure and prepare an un-mined E-boat for the escape—

Meanwhile, the frogmen had completed the first part of their task—

Darkness was their ally as they crept aboard their craft—

Made it! Now down below we go!

It won't be long before the others get here. Best check the engines first.

Right, let's go!

Immediately after the first explosion—

There's the big one—we've done it, boys!

Wow, we certainly made a mess of that, didn't we?

Destroyer off the port bow, sir!

Dead on time! Send the code-name 'Warlord' and stand by to board.

Yes, a perfect job, perfectly executed! Let's go home!

Welcome aboard, Warlord. Congratulations on the success of your mission.

A couple of weeks later—

You should be down there with 'em Flint, but there's no medals in our line of business.

I want no medals, sir. I lost ten men and that memory is all I'll ever need to remind me of the last cruise of the U-379!

Thanks, old son, but credit must go to these Navy chaps of yours and I'm going to see they get it. But first—what about some brekkers, eh?

The End